The Quest of Archimedes

The Quest
of Archimedes

BY TAD HARVEY
ILLUSTRATED BY SAM WISNOM

DOUBLEDAY & COMPANY, INC. • GARDEN CITY, NEW YORK

Other Books in This Series

THE QUEST OF GALILEO
THE QUEST OF ISAAC NEWTON
THE QUEST OF LOUIS PASTEUR
THE QUEST OF MICHAEL FARADAY
THE QUEST OF CAPTAIN COOK

Library of Congress Catalog Card Number 60-12175
Copyright © 1962 by Doubleday & Company, Inc.
All Rights Reserved
Printed in the United States of America
First Edition

Contents

An Ancient Modern Scientist

The year is 1906. In the city of Istanbul, Turkey, an elderly Danish scholar bends over a cracked and decaying roll of parchment. What he is able to read seems of no great historical importance. It is a church ritual copied down by Greek monks sometime around 1200 A.D. Many similar rituals have survived.

But the scholar still scrutinizes the manuscript. Often, he knows, Greek monks would scratch out texts they did not understand and write over them, for parchment was always scarce and costly. His trained eye detects unmistakable signs of this. Now, in order to uncover the buried text, he must treat the parchment with special chemicals, under artificial light rays.

What this scholar uncovered was a scientific treatise by Archimedes, called *On the Method*. Later, we will look at this treatise in detail and consider the full significance of its discovery. For the moment, let us simply consider what a famous historian of science recently said about *On the Method*. "It is one of the most revealing documents in the history, not only of ancient science, but of science in general at all times."

Those are astonishing words, if we remember that *On the Method* was written by an ancient Greek in the third century B.C. They suggest something quite remarkable about Archimedes: even now, in the middle of the twentieth century, science has a profound and reverent admiration for his work. Though he lived twenty-two centuries ago, Archimedes *thought* like today's scientists.

At the start of the Renaissance, when science began the great surge that would carry it to its twentieth-century heights, Archimedes' works were eagerly sought out and studied. The giants of that age—Galileo and Newton—turned back to him for instruction and guidance in both physics and mathematics. And his reputation has grown, not lessened, with the passing centuries. As one twentieth-century philosopher bluntly put it: "In the year 1500 Europe knew less than Archimedes, who died in the year 212 B.C."

Archimedes stood close to the dawn of the history of science. During his lifetime, as we will see, science was reaching its first great peak. As never before, the Greeks were observing the world around them and theorizing on what they saw.

But Greek science was also facing fundamental problems. It afforded few proven principles or methods on which Archimedes and other scientists could build.

10

Discovering ON THE METHOD

It was still searching for ways to approach the bewildering complexities of the natural world. In mathematics, the Greeks explored the use of numbers, pondered the relationships of different shapes, and wondered about the limits of mathematical calculation.

It was to these fundamental problems that Archimedes turned his brilliant and fertile mind. His was not so much a quest for new scientific facts as it was a quest for *methods* of reaching undisputed scientific truth. The methods he found pointed the way to the scientific advances of today, for they were "modern" to the very core.

Amid a Golden Age of Science

Suppose, for a moment, Archimedes could come to life today. You, a newspaper reporter, have been assigned to interview him. One of the first things you would want to get straight, naturally, is exactly what areas of science Archimedes represented. So, after a few preliminary questions, part of the published interview might read something like this:

Reporter: "Your great interest then, I take it, was always mathematics, 'pure math,' as we call it now— abstract geometry, arithmetic, numbers, methods of measurement, and so on. Is that correct?"

Archimedes: "Well, yes, first and foremost of course I was a theoretical mathematician. Math is the key to all my scientific work. But 'pure math' led me out in a great many different directions. Into what you call mechanical physics, for example. Every Greek knew you could lift tremendous weights by means of a lever.

ARCHIMEDES

But how could you determine what force you'd need in order to lift a certain weight with a certain lever? Was there a mathematical formula for it? Another branch of physics that intrigued me was hydrostatics: How could you predict what would happen to forces and weights in water, or under water? Then there was my work in astronomy. I once built a rather nice model of the solar system—sort of a miniature planetarium—accurate enough to predict eclipses of the sun and moon. Also, optics fascinated me at one point. That's the science of light and vision."

Reporter: "I see. But haven't I heard you were something of an inventor, too? And an engineer?"

Archimedes: "Yes, I suppose I was. But I am amazed to learn how many people think of me as nothing *but* an engineer and an inventor. Actually, my interest in the practical side of science was quite secondary. I certainly didn't devote my life to inventing and engineering. Of course, when it seemed my theoretical knowledge could help my government or my fellow citizens, then I felt I had to offer my services, and I sometimes learned things in the bargain. One of my inventions was the compound pulley. Another was the hydraulic screw—'Archimedes' screw,' it's now called —used for lifting water out of ships' holds and for similar jobs. It's just a screw spiraling inside a large pipe-like cylinder. Then I designed some war machines for the defense of my city, Syracuse. I suppose you could call me a military engineer. And a nautical engineer, too, since I was often called in to advise on special problems of designing, building, and launching ships."

Whatever else your interview with Archimedes might reveal, one conclusion would be inescapable. Archimedes was a remarkably versatile thinker. Mathematician, physicist, astronomer, inventor, military engineer, nautical engineer—Archimedes' mind ranged far and wide through both theoretical and applied science.

Yet, in a very real way, Archimedes was typical of his time. It was an age of great scientists with inquiring, versatile minds. These were Archimedes' contemporaries; many of them were his friends or teachers.

Like all great thinkers, Archimedes both shaped, and was shaped *by,* the age he lived in. There is little

question that he was the greatest mathematician, and one of the greatest over-all scientists, of the ancient world. But it would be wrong to think his greatness existed in a vacuum. He needed contact with other scientists, and he needed stimulation, even if it consisted only of seeing the shortcomings in other men's theories. The important thing was that there *were* scientific theories, and learned men to discuss and debate them.

The center of the scientific world in Archimedes' time was Alexandria, near the mouth of the Nile in Egypt. This city was the very heart and soul of Greek science. On any one day in the third century B.C., you were likely to find a selection of brilliant scientists in

ALEXANDER THE GREAT

Alexandria. Archimedes might be there, or any number of other great intellects. In fact, for over a hundred years there was hardly a scientist in the whole Greek empire who had not visited Alexandria at least once during his life. Nothing quite like it has existed ever since.

Alexandria's emergence as a capital of science was by no means an accident of history. It was due largely to the actions of two great rulers: Alexander the Great and Ptolemy I, king of Egypt.

It was Alexander the Great who chose the location of Alexandria in about 332 B.C. The city was then named and built in his honor.

During his short lifetime (356–23 B.C.) Alexander had conquered most of the known world. He pushed the frontiers of the Greek empire into North Africa, far into western Asia, and as far west as Spain. Greek culture began to spread out, away from the city-states such as Athens, and mingle with the other, older cultures around the Mediterranean. The two most important of these cultures were in Egypt and Mesopotamia. By absorbing the scientific insights of these older cultures, Greek science grew in wisdom and awareness.

Then, when Alexander died, the government of Egypt fell to one of his most gifted generals, Ptolemy. In 306 B.C., Ptolemy appointed himself king of Egypt —Ptolemy I, "The Savior"—and ruled for twenty years.

Ptolemy I was a shrewd and capable administrator, and he was determined to make Egypt the finest, richest, and most respected kingdom on the Mediterranean. Having chosen Alexandria as his capital, he called in the best architects and city planners to make it one of the most attractive and well-designed cities of the ancient world.

Fortunately for science, Ptolemy realized that wealth and prosperity alone would never gain Egypt, or himself, the sincere respect of the world. He set out to make Alexandria an intellectual center, too, as Athens was: a center of the arts, literature, and science.

Somehow, Ptolemy knew, he had to attract the attention of learned men in the cities and settlements all around the Mediterranean. He did this in a direct and brilliant manner.

First, Ptolemy built a special institute, the Museum of Alexandria, where philosophers, scientists, mathematicians, physicians, artists, and poets could meet, and work, and exchange ideas in a free and pleasant atmosphere. This museum had very little similarity to the museums of today. It got its name because it was supposed to be watched over by the Greek "Muses," nine imaginary goddesses of knowledge and creativity. Probably the closest thing to the Museum today would be the graduate school of a university.

Second, Ptolemy built a large and impressive library building and began stockpiling, by foul means and fair, all the learned writings he could find.

However questionable his motives and tactics, Ptolemy I eminently succeeded in making Alexandria one of the most active and influential intellectual communities in all history. For over a hundred years it was the spiritual home of Greek science. Like a great magnet, Alexandria drew to itself a host of bright intellects seeking knowledge and inspiration.

The first great scientist to appear in Alexandria was Strato the physicist. He came at the request of Ptolemy I, to be a tutor of the king's son. Strato had been educated in Athens at the Lyceum, the famous school of Aristotle (384–22 B.C.). There, Strato absorbed the physics of Aristotle and the mathematics of Plato (427–347 B.C.) and others.

Thus, Strato was a link between Athens and Alexandria: he brought the best of Greek science to Ptolemy and his son, the future Ptolemy II. Mainly through his influence, it is believed, the Museum became a place of scientific activity rather than an institution devoted strictly to the arts and philosophy.

Strato's work in physics was a continuation and somewhat of an improvement of Aristotle's. It is mainly interesting because it was the immediate forerunner of Archimedes' "modern" approach to physics.

Now, Aristotle's physics had had some glaring shortcomings. One big failing was that Aristotle had simply not made enough experiments or collected enough facts. Consequently, there were gaps and errors in his theories. Furthermore, Aristotle seldom used mathematics as a tool in his physical investigations. This was a tremendous oversight. Try to imagine taking a physics course today without knowing any math!

21

ARCHIMEDES AND EUCLID

Strato, too, all but ignored math in his physics; but he was a more thorough experimenter. For this reason, he corrected Aristotle on a number of points. Aristotle, for example, made a distinction between heavy and light bodies. Heavy bodies had "weight," he said, and tended to fall; light bodies had "lightness" and tended to rise. Rejecting this theory, Strato said that *all* bodies have weight. When the heavier ones fall, they merely push the lighter ones out, and upward. Strato's explanation, of course, is the correct one.

Soon after Strato, there arrived in Alexandria another man whose work would have an important effect on Archimedes. This was Euclid the geometer, author of the *Elements*. Until fifty years ago much of this great work was used as a high school geometry text *exactly* as Euclid had written it.

At one point, Euclid may have taught Archimedes geometry, but there is no definite proof of this. All we can say for certain is that Archimedes knew, and profited from, the *Elements*.

From Archimedes' own writings we learn about a great astronomer associated with the Museum: Aristarchus, "The Copernicus of Antiquity." In his treatise *The Sand Reckoner,* Archimedes tells us the most outstanding—and astounding—fact about Aristarchus: Eighteen centuries before Copernicus and Galileo, he put forth the theory that the sun stood still and the earth revolved around it.

Among the many other scientists who came to

23

Alexandria in this golden period, at least three were close friends of Archimedes. They were Eratosthenes, Conon, and Dositheos. Unfortunately, we know little about Conon, and even less about Dositheos. But Eratosthenes made it very hard for history to forget him. He lived a long and active life and did outstanding work in a great many different fields of learning.

Eratosthenes was an astronomer and a mathematician, the first mathematical geographer, and one of the world's first map makers. He was also a grammarian and a philologist, a literary critic, a historian, and a philosopher. Perhaps his most admirable scientific achievement was a very accurate estimate of the earth's circumference. Using both astronomy and geometry, he arrived at a circumference of 24,662 miles, which, considering his crude equipment, is amazingly close to modern science's 24,901.7 miles. Eratosthenes' measurement was important in another way. It gave, for the first time, a mathematical expression to the belief in a spherical rather than a flat earth. Not for seventeen hundred years would Magellan sail around the world and sweep away forever the stubborn belief in a flat earth.

Eratosthenes claimed still another "first." He was the first scientific librarian. In about 235 B.C., Ptolemy III appointed him director of the great Library of Alexandria. Thus, Eratosthenes began to turn the Library's huge accumulation of scientific knowledge, dating back in many fields to the dim beginnings of

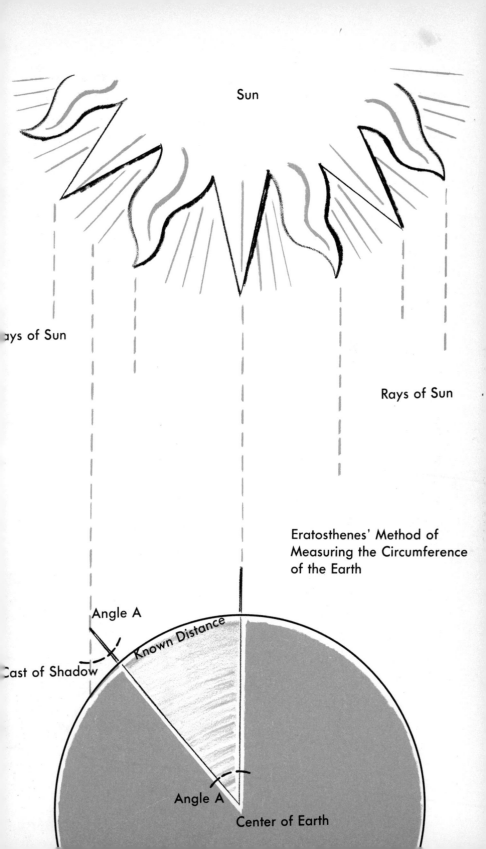

Sun

Rays of Sun

Rays of Sun

Eratosthenes' Method of
Measuring the Circumference
of the Earth

Angle A

Known Distance

Cast of Shadow

Angle A

Center of Earth

science in Egypt and Mesopotamia, into an orderly and usable body of knowledge.

In 1906, with the rediscovery of *On the Method*, Eratosthenes' scientific reputation was still further enhanced, for it was to him that Archimedes had dedicated this most significant of all his treatises.

About Archimedes' friend Dositheos, all we know is the little that Archimedes tells us in the prefaces to some of his works. Although he seems to have been a good deal younger, Dositheos was apparently Archimedes' closest friend in his later years. Also, since Archimedes dedicated four of his lengthiest and most

PLATO

ARISTOTLE

important geometrical works to him, we can safely say that Dositheos was a first-rate mathematician.

We know a little more about Conon. He was older than Dositheos and at one point had been his math teacher.

Apparently Conon died at an early age, a fact which Archimedes very much regretted both for personal and professional reasons. He and Conon had worked closely together, each submitting his newest ideas to the other for comment and criticism. In the preface to his geometrical treatise *On Spirals*, Archimedes writes sorrowfully of his dead friend: "Conon . . .

CONON

would have enriched geometry . . . For I know well that it was no common ability that he brought to bear on mathematics, and that his industry was extraordinary."

Conon was also an astronomer. He made a kind of astronomical calendar, giving the rising and setting times of the stars, and even some long-range weather predictions.

Curiously enough, these astronomical observations were not made from Alexandria, where Conon seems to have spent much of his life, but from Sicily and southern Italy. This suggests something extremely interesting about Conon and Archimedes. They may have been friends since childhood. As young men they may have worked and studied together in Syracuse, Sicily, the home and birthplace of Archimedes.

Let us turn there, from scholarly Alexandria, and see Archimedes against the backdrop of his own, less tranquil, native land.

Citizen of Syracuse

As the third century B.C. dawned, a long and bitter conflict was about to erupt between two peoples in the western Mediterranean. These were the Romans and the Carthaginians. From their capital, Carthage, on the northern tip of what is now Tunisia, the Carthaginians spread out in every direction, seeking control of all the western Mediterranean. Similarly, the Romans pushed down the boot of Italy, eager to expand their young nation. Between them lay Sicily, and its richest city, Syracuse.

It was here, in 287 B.C., that Archimedes was born. His life would be fatefully bound up in the approaching century-long struggle between Rome and Carthage, which we now know of as the Punic Wars.

Archimedes' father was Phidias, an astronomer. His astronomical works, if any, are lost, but Phidias must have been an able scientist, for Archimedes uses his father's calculations in one of his treatises.

For most of Archimedes' life, Syracuse was ruled by King Hiero II and then by Hiero's son, King Gelon II. The social setup of Syracuse was modeled after the ancient Greek city-states. Syracuse had, in fact, been founded by Greeks in the eighth century B.C. There were two social groups, citizens and slaves. The slaves did all the physical work, leaving the citizens free, ideally, to follow the theoretical pursuits of the mind.

Both Hiero and Gelon were great admirers of Archimedes and often called on him (as we will see later) for technical advice on various matters. Archimedes may even have been a member of the royal family.

Because of this close association with the rulers of Syracuse, Archimedes could undoubtedly have held a position in the government. But he chose not to and from an early age devoted himself entirely to mathematics and science.

At least twice during his life, Archimedes made the sea voyage to Alexandria. He remained there each time for several months, catching up on the newest ideas of the brilliant group of scientists that gathered about the Museum, and taking advantage of the great scientific collection in the Library. It was in Alexandria that Archimedes invented his hydraulic screw, probably at the request of Ptolemy II, who put it to use in controlling the sometimes devastating Nile floods.

Throughout Archimedes' lifetime, periodic battles flared in Sicily. Finally, in 214 B.C., the Roman general

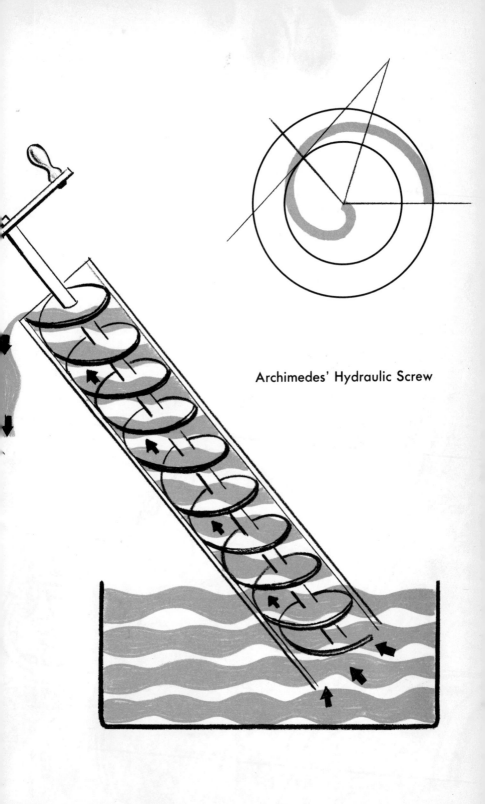

Archimedes' Hydraulic Screw

Marcellus decided to make an all-out effort to establish Roman rule firmly and forever over all Sicily. His most cherished—and crucial—objective was the conquest of Syracuse, and he began concentrating his land and sea forces around it.

Inside the walls of Syracuse, Archimedes, though now an old man of seventy-three, was still very much alive. He had prepared a warm reception for the attacking Romans.

Let Plutarch, the Greek writer of the first century A.D., tell us about it:

"Marcellus . . . proceeded to attack the city both by land and sea. The land forces were conducted by Appius: Marcellus, with sixty galleys, each with five

rows of oars, furnished with all sorts of arms and missiles, and a huge bridge of planks laid upon eight ships chained together, upon which was carried the engine to cast stones and darts, assaulted the walls . . ."

When they saw Marcellus' mighty land and sea forces approaching, Plutarch continues, "the Syracusans were struck dumb with fear, thinking that nothing would avail against such violence and power. But Archimedes began to work his engines and hurled against the land forces all sorts of missiles and masses of stone, which came down with incredible noise and speed; nothing at all could ward off their weight, but they knocked down in heaps those who stood in the way and threw the ranks in disorder. Furthermore, beams were suddenly thrown over the ships from the walls,

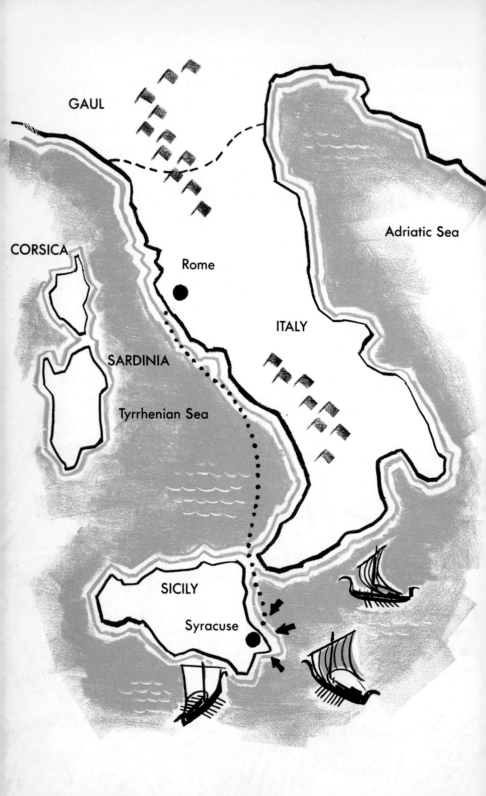

GAUL

Adriatic Sea

CORSICA

Rome

ITALY

SARDINIA

Tyrrhenian Sea

SICILY

Syracuse

and some of the ships were sent to the bottom by means of weights fixed to beams and plunging down from above; others were drawn up by iron claws, or crane-like beaks, attached to the prow and were plunged down on their sterns, or were twisted round and turned about by means of ropes within the city, and dashed against the cliffs . . . with great destruction of the crews, who were crushed to pieces . . . As for the engine which Marcellus was bringing up from the platform of ships . . . while it was still some distance away, as it was being carried to the wall, a stone ten talents in weight [about 1800 pounds] was discharged at it, and after this a second and a third; some of these, falling upon it with a great crash and sending up a wave, crushed the base of the engine, shook the framework and dislodged it from the barrier, so that Marcellus in perplexity sailed away in his ships and passed the word to his land forces to retire."

Believing that Archimedes' war machines were only effective at long-range, Marcellus slipped a large number of troops in close to Syracuse's walls under cover of darkness.

"But Archimedes, it seems, had long ago prepared for such a contingency engines adapted to all distances and missiles of short range and, through openings in the wall, small in size but many and continuous, short-ranged engines called scorpions could be trained on objects close at hand without being seen by the enemy . . .

"In the end the Romans became so filled with fear that if they saw a little piece of rope or wood projecting over the wall, they cried, 'There it is! Archimedes is training some engine on us!' and fled; seeing this, Marcellus abandoned all fighting and assault, and for the future relied on a long seige."

Through no fault of military engineer Archimedes, Marcellus finally captured Syracuse after a two-year siege. He did so, probably, in the only way he could have: by trickery, and with the help of some traitors inside the city. A few hours after Marcellus' forces entered the city, Archimedes was dead, slain by a Roman soldier.

There are several different versions of Archimedes' death, but the one most often told is this. Unaware that Syracuse was lost, Archimedes had become absorbed in a geometrical problem and was drawing diagrams in the earth of his yard. Suddenly the figure of a Roman soldier loomed over him. "Marcellus," the soldier barked, "wants to see you *at once!*" Archimedes hardly heard him. All he noticed was that the soldier had stepped on his diagrams. "Get off my diagrams!" he shouted. Enraged, the soldier pulled out his sword and killed Archimedes on the spot.

About this story, the twentieth-century philosopher Alfred North Whitehead once rather bitterly remarked: "The death of Archimedes at the hands of a Roman soldier is symbolical of a world change of the first magnitude. The Romans were a great race, but . . .

they were not dreamers enough to arrive at new points of view, which could give more fundamental control over the forces of nature. No Roman ever lost his life because he was absorbed in the contemplation of a mathematical diagram."

The last human being to report any trace of Archimedes was the great Roman orator and politician Cicero. When he was quaestor of Sicily, in 75 B.C., Cicero discovered the crumbling tomb of Archimedes near Syracuse. On it, he saw, had been chiseled one of Archimedes' favorite geometrical theorems, a perfect sphere enclosed in a perfect cylinder. Although Cicero restored the tomb, the passing centuries have covered it up again, and its location is unknown today.

Many stories have come down to us that picture Archimedes as a classic model of the "absent-minded scientist." The story of his death, in a way, is one of these. But there are some far less brutal ones.

Plutarch, for example, writes that Archimedes, wrapped in the study of some mathematical problem, often forgot to eat for long periods. Furthermore, he utterly neglected his physical appearance. His friends often had practically to drag him to the Syracusan baths. There, far from being daunted, Archimedes continued to think out his problem, drawing diagrams in the ashes of the hearth fires and even in the oil that had been rubbed on his own body.

Such stories, probably, are not literally true. But there is undoubtedly a core of truth in them. Many mathematicians *are* rather unworldly. There are examples of this in our own day. Theoretical, abstract mathematics can be very far removed from the things of this world, and it requires the deepest and most unbroken concentration.

Thus, Archimedes may very well have been an "absent-minded scientist." From the standpoint of modern science, however, he was far more precise and worldly than almost all his contemporaries.

Here are some of the reasons.

One of modern science's chief characteristics is its firm basis in mathematics. Physics, chemistry, even biology, depend heavily on mathematical expressions and techniques. It would be almost impossible to extract the mathematics from these sciences, so deeply is it woven into them.

This was far from true in the time of Archimedes. For a long time, the Greeks had made a sharp distinction between mathematics, especially geometry, and those sciences that dealt with tangible, physical things.

Aristotle, we know, used little math in his physics and consequently made many false assumptions.

In the same way, Plato kept all physical considerations out of his geometry. Mathematics, he felt, should be purely a matter of the intellect. It should avoid all contact with the sordid physical world.

Plato carried this view to amazing extremes. He once became enraged at a mathematician who had devised a new and useful instrument for drawing geometrical figures. The only instruments a geometer should use, Plato said, were a ruler and a compass. Anything else would "soil" mathematics. This attitude led Plato to make some utterly fantastic speculations about the mathematical nature of the universe, which had no imaginable relation to reality.

Archimedes admired abstract mathematics fully as much as Plato. But his mind was too realistic and penetrating to accept Plato's extreme views. He saw the great advantage that could be gained by joining mathematics with tangible things and physical facts. In this direction lay the greatest triumphs of modern science.

A Shape, a Length, a Very Large Number

What awes present-day mathematicians most about Archimedes is that he accomplished so much without the benefit of today's advanced techniques. He just *couldn't* have made some of his mathematical discoveries. But he did. Wrote one scientist in the 1950s: "Archimedes' achievements pass our imagination, they are almost weird."

Today's mathematicians point out that only by using a form of calculus could Archimedes have reached some of his conclusions about shapes, and solids, and curves. Yet calculus was not formally invented until the seventeenth century. Also, certain of his discoveries seem to require a knowledge of trigonometry and advanced algebra. Yet Archimedes could have known no system of trigonometry and only a primitive kind of algebra. What we recognize as an algebraic equation just did not exist in Archimedes' time.

43

a

b

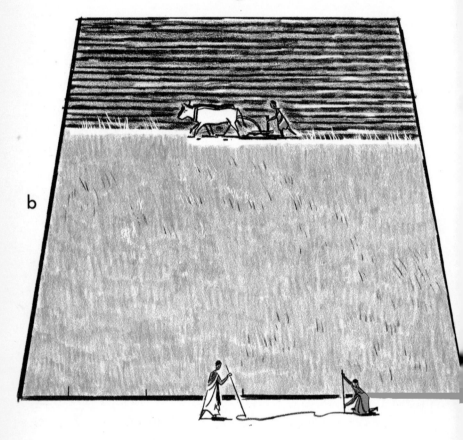

ab = Area of Field

Furthermore, the Greek number system that Archimedes inherited was far more clumsy than our decimal system. Fractions, too, were still developing. Archimedes sometimes used unit fractions—those with a numerator of one. Thus, he might write the fraction five sixths ($\frac{5}{6}$) as one half plus one third ($\frac{1}{2} + \frac{1}{3}$).

These contrasts between Greek mathematics and our own serve to show the genius and resourcefulness of Archimedes. But Greek mathematics itself should not be underrated. It had progressed a long way, over a long period of time, and had made impressive gains. Besides, Archimedes was very much a Greek mathematician, both in his attitudes and in the kind of answers he sought.

Before looking at Archimedes' own achievements, therefore, let's look briefly at Greek mathematics.

Its roots lay in Egypt and Mesopotamia, thousands of years before Archimedes was born.

In Mesopotamia, the Babylonian people used a rough and ready geometry for finding the areas of fields—in other words, for surveying. They saw that the area of a square or oblong field could be found by multiplying two of its adjacent sides (modern formula: area $= ab$); likewise, they saw that a triangle could be considered half an oblong (modern formula: area $= \frac{1}{2}ab$). When it came to measuring the area of an irregularly shaped field, they merely cut it up into rough oblongs and triangles, which they could measure, and then added the several areas together to get the total area.

The Egyptians were masters of architectural geometry, as one look at their great pyramids shows. These were designed and built according to strict geometrical specifications.

It seems that the Egyptians went a little further than the Babylonians in geometry. For example, they learned how to find the volume of a cylindrical silo used for storing grain and the volume of a frustum of one of their pyramids.

Despite minor differences, though, the geometries of Egypt and Mesopotamia were very similar in one respect: both were used entirely for solving practical problems, as in building and surveying. They were alike in another way. Neither geometry offered any completely general formulas for finding the areas of different geometric figures. When an Egyptian or a Babylonian set out to measure a triangular field, he did not carry in his head a formula, area $= \frac{1}{2}ab$. Instead, he carried an "example problem," already solved, showing how the area of one specific triangle had been found. By following the steps in the example problem and substituting his own measurements, he found the area of his field.

At this stage, the Greeks took up geometry. They transformed it into something entirely different from the practical geometry of the Babylonians and Egyptians. Instead of thinking about triangular fields, the Greeks began to think about triangles themselves, triangles as imaginary and perfect figures which, at the very most, could be represented by fine lines on paper. Mathematics became an abstract and theoretical study, having little to do with practical problems.

Simultaneously, the Greeks began to seek general

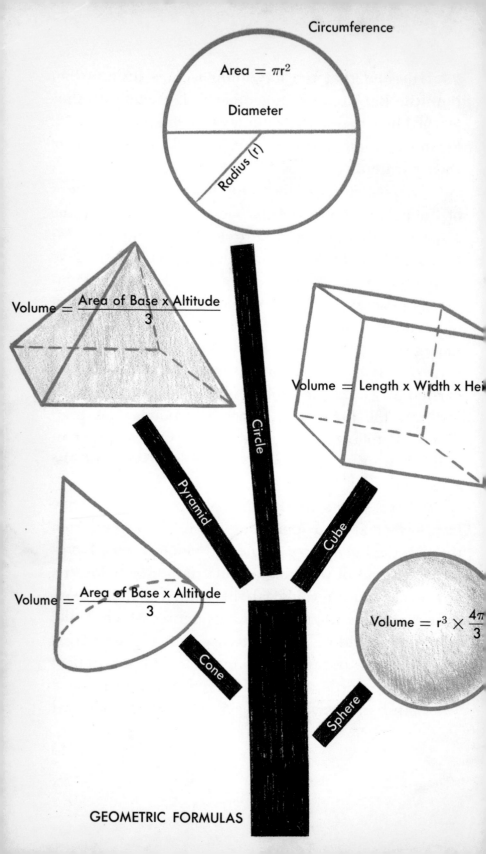

Circumference

Area $= \pi r^2$

Diameter

Radius (r)

Volume $= \dfrac{\text{Area of Base x Altitude}}{3}$

Volume $=$ Length x Width x Hei

Circle

Pyramid

Cube

Volume $= \dfrac{\text{Area of Base x Altitude}}{3}$

Volume $= r^3 \times \dfrac{4\pi}{3}$

Cone

Sphere

GEOMETRIC FORMULAS

solutions for geometrical problems. They wanted to find formulas that *always* worked in finding the areas or volumes of *any* given type of geometrical figure: one formula for the area of all circles, one formula for the volume of all spheres, and so on.

Finding general formulas for abstract figures—finding general things you can say about their properties and relationships—was, actually, the basic aim of all Greek geometry. This includes the work of Archimedes.

Naturally, as Greek mathematics became more abstract and generalized, its connections with the everyday world became less and less obvious. The farm fields of Egypt and Mesopotamia dropped far into the background.

This bothered many Greeks. They began to question whether their mathematics had any relation to reality at all. Was mathematics, perhaps, nothing but a ridiculous fantasy?

One such questioner was Zeno, who lived in the fifth century B.C. He criticized Greek mathematical thought on a number of fundamental points and very nearly destroyed abstract mathematics before it had a chance to get started. But the questions he raised *had* to be raised, and mathematicians grew wiser in trying to answer them.

Zeno is most famous for his puzzle of Achilles and the tortoise. These two, said Zeno, were having a race. Since Achilles ran ten times as fast as the tortoise, he

Start

had given the tortoise a head start of one tenth of a mile. When, Zeno asked, would Achilles catch and overtake the tortoise? It was obvious to everybody that Achilles *would* catch up, and very soon.

But according to mathematics, Zeno showed, Achilles would never quite catch up; for as Achilles ran one tenth of a mile, the tortoise would crawl one hundredth of a mile, and as Achilles ran that one hundredth of a mile, the tortoise would crawl another one thousandth of a mile. Thus, the distance between

50

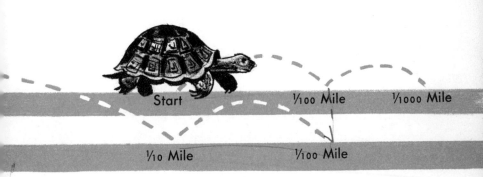

Start   ¹/₁₀₀ Mile   ¹/₁₀₀₀ Mile

¹/₁₀ Mile   ¹/₁₀₀ Mile

them would get smaller and smaller ($\frac{1}{10}$ mi., $\frac{1}{100}$ mi., $\frac{1}{1000}$ mi.) until it was *almost* nothing, but the tortoise would always be a little ahead.

Here was an example of abstract mathematics directly contradicting something everyone knew to be true. Zeno's puzzle implied that mathematical calculation was not only incapable of obtaining accurate measurements and other results but was also incapable of representing the world as it really was.

Greek mathematicians realized that criticisms like

those of Zeno were somewhat far-fetched. But the Greeks also realized that such criticisms challenged the whole idea of mathematics as a useful tool. Such challenges had to be met, at least on a practical level.

They were met, principally, by a Greek named Eudoxus (408–355 B.C.). He asked his fellow mathematicians to make a fundamental assumption. "Let us assume," said Eudoxus, "that if there are two lengths, we can always find a multiple of one that exceeds the other."

To put Eudoxus' assumption in more specific terms, suppose one line is one billionth of a foot long and another line is a billion feet long. It will always be possible, says Eudoxus, to find a large enough number by which you can multiply one billionth of a foot to get a length longer than a billion feet. The number, of course, would have to be tremendously large. But it would never be greater than any imaginable number. It would never be *infinite*.

Isn't Eudoxus' assumption completely obvious and self-evident? It certainly seems so. But there is absolutely no way to prove it.

About its usefulness, however, there is not the slightest question. Look again at the puzzle of Achilles and the tortoise and see how Eudoxus helps us.

Suppose the distance (or length) Achilles runs in one second is thirty feet. In the same second, the tortoise, with his head start of one tenth of a mile, crawls three feet. To find the distance each travels, we would multiply thirty feet and three feet, respectively, by the number of seconds elapsed since the start of the race. As the race goes on, therefore, we keep multiplying three feet and thirty feet by a greater and greater number. Eventually we will reach a multiple of thirty feet (the distance Achilles runs) that exceeds one tenth of a mile (the tortoise's head start) plus the product of three feet and the elapsed number of seconds (the distance the tortoise crawls). Achilles, this time, mathematically wins the race.

Eudoxus' assumption about lengths was part of Archimedes' mathematical inheritance, and Archimedes accepted the inheritance with gratitude, for it provided an essential foundation for all of his own mathematical thought.

In fact, so strikingly did Archimedes once apply Eudoxus' assumption that it has been known ever since as the Axiom of Archimedes.

The striking application occurs in his treatise *The Sand Reckoner*. Archimedes sets out in this remarkable work to do nothing less than count the grains of sand that could be stuffed into the universe. He begins:

"There are some, King Gelon, who think that the number of sand is infinite in multitude; and I mean by the sand not only that which exists about Syracuse and the rest of Sicily but also that which is found in every region whether inhabited or uninhabited. Again, there are some who, without regarding it as infinite, yet think that no number has been named which is

great enough to exceed it in multitude. . . . But I will try to show you by means of geometrical proofs, which you will be able to follow, that, of the numbers named by me, . . . some exceed not only the number of the mass of sand equal in magnitude to the earth filled up in the way described, but also that of a mass equal in magnitude to the universe."

54

Basically, what Archimedes wants to prove to King Gelon is that there is a multiple of a sand grain that exceeds the volume of the universe. This, we see, is merely the Axiom of Archimedes applied to volumes rather than lengths.

There are, however, two related problems: (1) What is the size of the universe? (2) Is there a number big enough to express the multiple of a sand grain that would fill up the universe?

By putting together the calculations of various astronomers—among them Aristarchus and Phidias, his own father—Archimedes arrives at what he considers a safe figure for the maximum size of the universe. (In our time, of course, many scientists no longer think of the universe as having a measurable "size," believing it to be infinite.)

Once he has the size of the universe, Archimedes begins to fill it up with sand grains. No more than ten thousand sand grains, he shows, could fit in a poppy seed. No more than forty poppy seeds fill a thimble; no more than a certain number of thimbles fill a typical Greek stadium. Step by step, Archimedes increases the volume of sand grains.

As they pile up, they outstrip the ability of the Greek number system to express their quantity. But Archimedes is ready for this emergency. He has *created* a number system that can express very large numbers simply and concisely. His system is more than adequate to handle the sand grains. The largest number in his system, if we were to write it all out, would require up to eighty thousand million million digits. By comparison, the number of sand grains in Archimedes' universe is tiny: a mere 10^{63}, or the number ten followed by sixty-three zeros.

Archimedes wrote another treatise that involved tremendously large numbers. This was *The Cattle Problem*. It is an exercise in what modern scientists call "indeterminate analysis."

An indeterminate equation is one with two or more unknowns. A problem in indeterminate analysis can have any number of equations, but there is always one *less* equation than the number of unknowns. Such problems can have any number of solutions. (Remember, here, that Archimedes did not have equations, and he had to state the problem some other way.) Mathematicians are often interested in finding the smallest and simplest numbers that will solve a problem in indeterminate analysis.

For example, the one equation

$$x - y = 1$$

has two unknowns. It can be solved with the numbers 7865 and 7864 and millions of others. But the simplest positive whole numbers that solve it are $x = 2, y = 1$.

In *The Cattle Problem,* Archimedes asks the reader to compute the number of cattle who (he claims) "once upon a time grazed on the fields of the Thrinacian isle of Sicily." He divides the total number into eight groups and asks the reader to compute the number of cattle in each group. Thus, there are not a mere two unknowns, but eight:

$$X = \text{the number of white bulls}$$
$$x = \text{the number of white cows}$$
$$Y = \text{the number of black bulls}$$
$$y = \text{the number of black cows}$$
$$Z = \text{the number of yellow bulls}$$
$$z = \text{the number of yellow cows}$$
$$W = \text{the number of dappled bulls}$$
$$w = \text{the number of dappled cows}$$

Each of these groups, says Archimedes, bears a certain relation to some of the other groups. The white bulls, for example, are equal to five-sixths of the black bulls plus all the yellow bulls ($X = \frac{5}{6}Y + Z$). He gives seven such equations for the eight unknowns.

The total number of cattle, as computed by one twentieth-century mathematician, cannot be less than some five trillion, or, to be exact: 5,916,837,175,686. Interpreting the problem a different way, another mathematician estimated that it would require seven hundred pages of fine print to write out all eight "simplest" numbers that satisfy the equations. Whatever the correct figure, Archimedes' herd would find "the isle of Sicily" a tight squeeze!

Archimedes himself probably did not even try to work out the problem exactly, though we can be certain he came to some approximate solution. What is

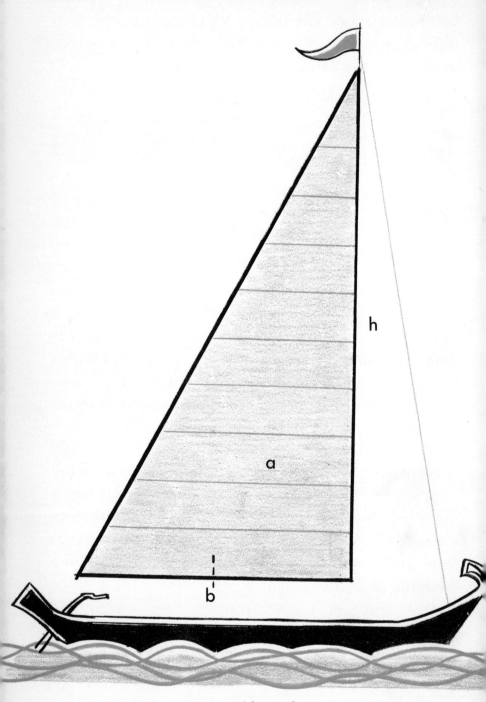

$$a = \tfrac{1}{2}b \times h$$

significant is that Archimedes *knew* such an immensely difficult and complex problem could be solved, long before mathematicians formally developed the methods to solve it.

In the field of geometry, doubters like Zeno also had a profound effect on the work of Archimedes and other Greek mathematicians. The doubter said to the geometers: "You may *claim* the area of any triangle is always equal to one half its base times its height, and I may believe you. But what if I don't believe you? How can you demonstrate to me that it is undeniably true? How can you prove it?"

Here, the whole problem of demonstrating proof was raised. And here, Archimedes was a master. "It is not possible to find in geometry," writes Plutarch, "more difficult and troublesome questions or proofs set out in simpler and clearer terms."

In his proofs of geometrical theorems, Archimedes used what is called the "method of exhaustion." It is based on the fact that it is easier to prove the formula for a rectilinear figure (one bounded by straight lines) than it is to prove formulas for curvilinear figures (those bounded by curved lines). In the method of exhaustion, you construct a rectilinear figure that fits as closely as possible inside and/or outside a curvilinear figure, then mathematically "exhaust"—use up—the space still remaining between the curved lines and the straight lines.

A crude case of the method of exhaustion would

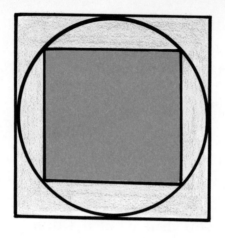

be to construct a perfect square as closely as possible around a perfect circle, and a second square that fitted as closely as possible inside the circle. Then, if you averaged the areas of the two squares, the result would be somewhere close to the area of the circle. Archimedes was tremendously more precise. In a similar case, instead of using four-sided squares, he used rectilinear figures with ninety-six equal sides.

Jointly with the method of exhaustion, Archimedes used the trick of logic called "reduction to absurdity." He would state that what he wanted to prove was *not* true. Then, in a series of logical steps, he would show that such a statement could only lead to a contradiction of some theorem that had already been accepted as undeniably true. Therefore, he concluded, if the exact opposite of what he wished to prove was false, then what he wished to prove must be true.

Using such methods of proof, Archimedes demonstrated the truth of many geometrical theorems. He showed that the volume of a sphere is always two thirds of the volume of an enclosing cylinder. (This is the theorem Cicero found on Archimedes' tomb.) He proved the formula for the volume of a sphere and for the area of a sphere's surface. He gave a highly accurate value for π (pronounced "pie": the ratio of the circumference to the diameter of a circle), which was very, very close to modern math's value of 3.14159265. He established formulas for areas bounded by the curve called a parabola and formulas for areas bounded by the gracefully curving line we now call Archimedes' spiral.

Proof, however, is one thing. Discovery is another. Proof is the formal, logical statement of a discovery, designed to convince the most doubtful critic. But to prove something, a scientist must already have discovered—or, at the very least, strongly suspected—the true answer before he begins. This leads to a very interesting question.

How did Archimedes make his mathematical discoveries?

Part of the answer is that Archimedes, in many situations, used the equivalents of modern mathematical methods. True, he knew no formal system of calculus, or trigonometry, or advanced algebra. But when he reached a point in his investigations where Greek mathematics could no longer help him, Archimedes instinctively grasped and applied these modern methods. That he could do so, present-day mathematicians feel, is nothing short of miraculous.

There is more to the answer.

In 1906, as we know, *On the Method* was discovered. Its contents would have shocked Plato to the quick. Plato would have wanted to expel Archimedes forever from the brotherhood of mathematicians.

To make some of his discoveries, *On the Method* revealed, Archimedes had considered ideal geometric shapes as if they were physical objects, having weight and substance. He weighed, as on a balance scale, a geometrical figure whose properties he knew against one whose properties he wanted to find. Then, by

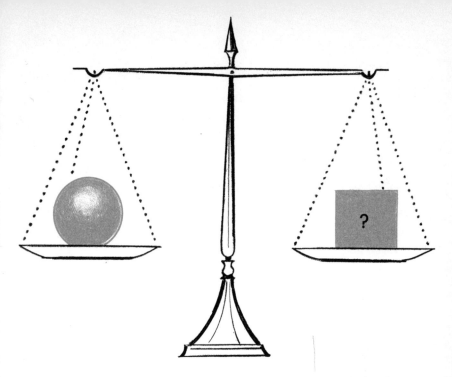

applying a mechanical principle, the law of the lever, he could get a very clear idea of the properties of the unknown figure and its relation to the known figure on the other side of the balance.

On the Method is almost unique in the annals of science. Only a handful of scientists have ever been able to retrace the mental steps which led them to the brink of a discovery. Practically none has been able to present those steps in a formal scientific paper. This is so because scientific discoveries tend to be based at least partly on intuition and momentary flashes of insight, which are very hard to explain in a logical and coherent manner. *On the Method* is indeed "one of the most revealing documents in the history . . . of science in general at all times."

With the writing of *On the Method*, Archimedes broke through the wall that Plato and others had built between mathematics and the physical world. He made his greatest mathematical discoveries because he applied a physical law to mathematics.

Now, let us see what happened when Archimedes did the reverse: applied mathematics to physics and mechanics.

Through the Doorway of Modern Science

Almost everyone at one time has ridden a seesaw and knows how it works. If the person on the other side of the seesaw weighs about the same as you, both of you can easily manage to balance in mid-air. You are in equilibrium. But if your weights are somewhat different, the heavier person will sink to the ground and send the lighter one aloft. However, most seesaws allow for different weights: they are built so you can move the board one way or another on its support (scientific term: fulcrum). Then, if you move the board toward the lighter person, it will again be possible for you to balance. If you move the board *too* far toward the lighter person, he will be able to lift the heavier one aloft.

In his treatise *On the Equilibrium of Planes*, Archimedes gave the principle behind these physical facts: Two bodies balance at distances from the fulcrum which are reciprocally proportional to their weights.

100 LBS.

4 Feet

12 Feet

50 LBS.

8 Feet

The truth of this principle has never been challenged. Physics students learn it today, for it is of basic importance in understanding the mechanics of forces and weights.

As an illustration, suppose a child weighs fifty pounds and his mother weighs one hundred pounds. They want to balance on a twelve-foot seesaw. Since the child weighs exactly half as much as his mother, he would have to be exactly twice as far from the seesaw's fulcrum to balance her. This distance is eight feet. The mother, weighing twice as much, would have to be half as far from the fulcrum, or four feet.

We see that eight feet bears the same proportion to four feet as one hundred pounds bears to fifty pounds. Eight is twice four. One hundred is twice fifty. The distances are "reciprocally proportional" to the weights.

Of course, in real life, things would never work out so neatly. The seesaw board might be unevenly cut or slightly off center on the fulcrum. Mother or child might lean slightly or shift position. Scientists call such possibilities "variables."

Archimedes knew perfectly well that his principle did not account for variables. In fact, he arrived at it by sensing that two equal and perfect geometrical figures would "balance" at equal distances from a central geometric point. Furthermore, he had assumed that physical objects had a "center of gravity"—a theoretical point at which their full weight might be considered to be concentrated. Thus, his principle was an idealized mathematical statement. Archimedes the modern scientist was at work.

All the laws of modern physics are stated exactly like this one. They do not account for variables. This is their greatest strength. Instead of getting bogged down in a mass of irrelevant and often misleading details, a mathematical law cuts straight through to the general truth. Then it is usually a routine matter for a scientist to incorporate any significant variables into the final answer.

From his principle of equilibrium it was an easy step for Archimedes to the principle of the lever. They are, actually, one and the same principle. We saw that a fifty-pound child could balance his one-hundred-pound mother if the child was twice as far from the fulcrum as his mother. Now, if we increase the child's distance from the fulcrum a little more—say, from eight feet to nine feet—then he would be able to lift his mother upward. Here, the seesaw board would be working as a lever, enabling the child to lift twice his own weight.

His understanding of levers apparently led Archimedes to invent many sorts of effort-saving machines, such as the compound pulley and the windlass. In this connection, there is a fascinating story told by Plutarch:

"Archimedes . . . wrote [to King Hiero] that with a given force it was possible to move any given weight; and emboldened, as it is said, by the strength of the proof, he averred that, if there were another world and he could go to it, he could move this one. Hiero was amazed and besought him to give a practical demonstration of the problem and show some great object moved by some small force; he thereupon chose a three-masted merchantman among the king's ships which had been hauled on shore with great labor by a large band of men, and after putting on board many men and the usual cargo, sitting some distance away and without any special effort, he pulled gently with his hand at the end of a compound pulley and drew

the vessel smoothly and evenly towards himself as though she were running along the surface of the water."

Stories such as this are not mere side lights to the more serious aspects of Archimedes' work. They have a significance of their own, for they illustrate just how modern Archimedes really was.

By developing devices like the compound pulley from ideal scientific principles, Archimedes pointed the way to our modern industrial and technological advances. He strikingly showed how "pure science" could put new and powerful tools in the hands of men.

Think back also to Plutarch's description of the siege of Syracuse. There can be no doubt that the devastating and unprecedented "engines" Archimedes built were based on scientific principles of levers and pulleys and weights. There is a direct line between Archimedes the mechanical physicist and the twentieth-century nuclear physicists who built the atomic bomb from their theoretical knowledge of atoms.

Apparently King Hiero fully realized Archimedes' usefulness and called on him continually to solve one problem or another. It would be interesting to know how Archimedes himself, whose first love was always theoretical science, felt about these constant intrusions on his time. (There may be a clue in the fact that, so far as we know, Archimedes never dedicated even one treatise to King Hiero.)

At any rate, when King Hiero, "a zealous shipbuilder," decided he wanted to build a mammoth grain freighter, he enlisted Archimedes as his technical adviser.

The exact dimensions of this ship have been lost, but we know it was capable of carrying some thirty-five hundred tons of cargo and required enough materials to build sixty average-sized ships. Furthermore, it was probably one of the most luxurious ships of all time. According to the third-century-A.D. Greek historian Athenaeus, it had "a gymnasium and promenades . . . garden beds of every sort luxuriant with plants of marvelous growth . . . bowers of white ivy

and grape vines . . . a shrine of Aphrodite . . . walls and ceilings of cypress wood, and doors of ivory and fragrant cedar . . . a library . . . ten stalls for horses . . . a water tank at the bow with a capacity of twenty thousand gallons . . . a fish tank . . . and the whole ship was adorned with appropriate paintings."

With all these elaborate refinements, however, Archimedes had nothing whatever to do. His contributions were far more down to earth.

When the hull had been completed, Athenaeus tells us, "this part of the ship . . . was ordered to be launched in the sea, that it might receive the finishing touches there. But after considerable discussion in regard to the method of pulling it into the water, Archimedes the mechanician alone was able to launch

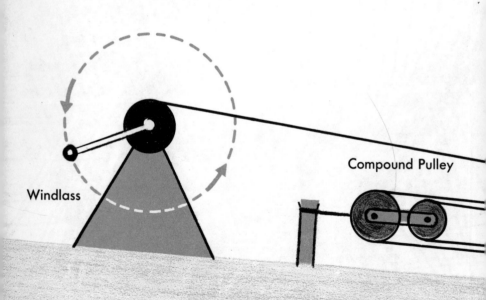

Windlass

Compound Pulley

it with the help of a few persons. For by the construction of a windlass, he was able to launch a ship of so great proportions into the water. Archimedes was the first to invent the construction of the windlass."

Next, Archimedes the military engineer went to work: "A wall with battlements and decks athwart the ship was built on supports; on this stood a stone hurler, which could shoot by its own power a stone weighing one hundred and eighty pounds or a javelin eighteen feet long. This engine was constructed by Archimedes. Either one of these missiles could be hurled six hundred feet."

Archimedes' "stone hurler" probably most resembled a gigantic crossbow, with a thick, strong rope as

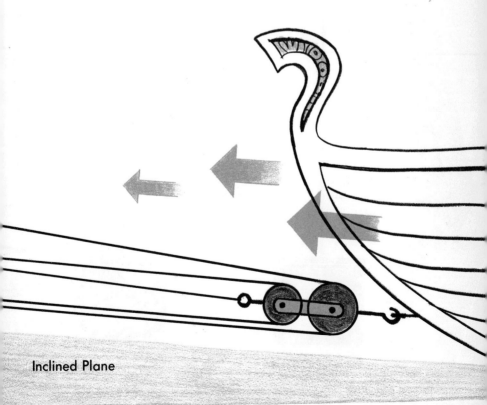

Inclined Plane

a bowstring. Undoubtedly Archimedes equipped it with some kind of crank or lever for creating tremendous tension in the bow and rope. And he would have devised some kind of triggerlike mechanism to hold and release this tension—sending stone or javelin instantly toward an enemy.

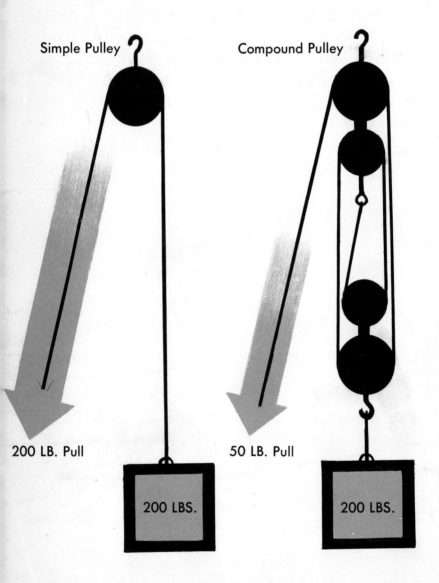

Simple Pulley

Compound Pulley

200 LB. Pull

50 LB. Pull

200 LBS.

200 LBS.

Stone Hurler

Finally, a device that Archimedes had invented many years before, in Alexandria, was installed as standard equipment: "The bilge water, even when it became very deep, could easily be pumped out by one man with the aid of a screw, an invention of Archimedes."

This colossal grain ship had a rather undignified end. After it had been completed and lay, in all its glory, off the coast of Syracuse, Hiero got a jolting bit of news: no harbor on the Mediterranean could handle it. What on earth, Hiero wondered, could he do with it?

Hiero solved the problem quite nicely. He sent the ship as a "present" to King Ptolemy IV of Egypt, thereby making himself look magnificently generous. At Alexandria, it had to be hauled up on shore by the efforts of thousands, and there it stayed.

No doubt Archimedes was very irked at King Hiero. He had put a great deal of effort and ingenuity into his work on the wheat ship, and it could hardly please him to think of the ship settling into the sand on the shores of Egypt.

Soon, however, Archimedes was engaged in another project for King Hiero. The results of this project would have a far longer life than the oversized grain freighter. What he found was "Archimedes' Principle," and it is part of every basic physics course taught today.

Hiero, it seems, wanted a solid-gold crown made, which he could give as an offering to the gods. He had given the royal goldsmith a certain amount of gold for this purpose. After the goldsmith had made and delivered the crown, Hiero, for some reason, became suspicious. He suspected that the goldsmith had used some silver in the crown and kept a part of the more precious gold for himself. But how could Hiero prove it? He turned, naturally, to Archimedes.

According to the first-century-B.C. Latin writer Vitruvius, the answer came to Archimedes while he was taking a bath, and Archimedes ". . . without a moment's delay and transported with joy . . . jumped out of the tub and rushed home naked, crying out in a loud voice that he had found what he was seeking; for as he ran he shouted repeatedly in Greek, '*Eureka! Eureka!*'"

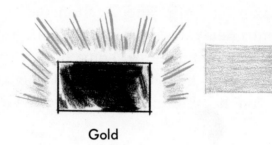

Gold

Silver

False Crown

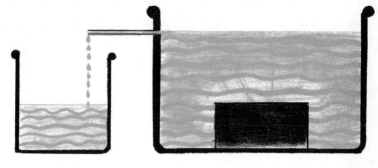

1 LB.

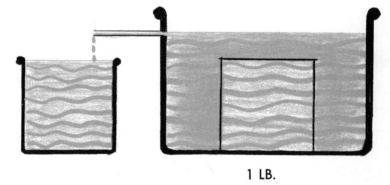

1 LB.

1 LB.

Whether Vitruvius' tale is true or not, Archimedes could have noticed two relevant things in his bath. First, as he settled more and more of his body into the water, the water rose higher and higher in the tub. Second, when he was almost fully immersed in water, he could support his weight on his fingertips.

In turn, this would suggest two general rules to Archimedes: (1) a body displaces (pushes aside) water in equal proportion to the amount (volume) of the body submerged and (2) a body loses weight in water. From two such observations, it is a logical step to the first law of hydrostatics, otherwise known as Archimedes' Principle: a body wholly or partly immersed in a fluid is pushed upward by a force equal in weight to the weight of the volume of the fluid it displaces. This principle was later found to be just as valid for objects wholly or partly immersed in a gas, such as air.

Here are two specific examples of Archimedes' Principle. Suppose a stone weighing 100 pounds has a volume of one cubic foot. The stone therefore displaces one cubic foot of water. Since a cubic foot of water weighs 62.4 pounds, the water will exert that amount of upward force on the stone. Thus, if we weighed the stone in water, it would weigh 62.4 pounds *less,* or 37.6 pounds. Now, take a 50-pound block of wood with a volume of one cubic foot. Since the upward force of water (62.4 pounds) exceeds the weight of the wood (50 pounds), the wood floats.

In using the principle to solve the problem of

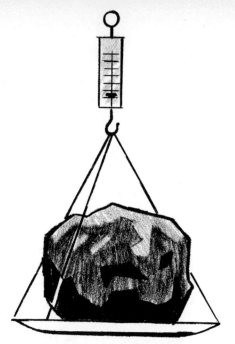

100 LBS. = Weight in Air

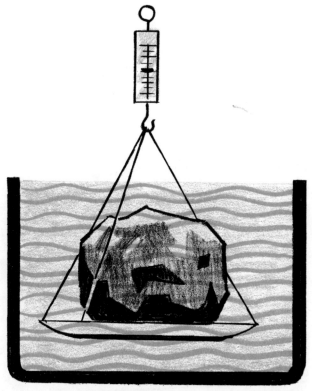

37.6 LBS. = Weight in Water

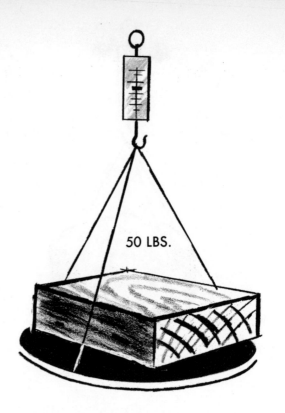

50 LBS.

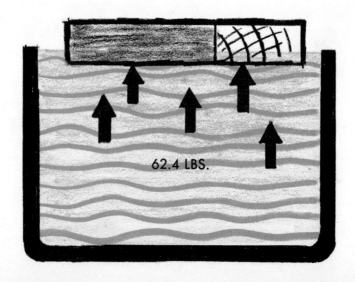

62.4 LBS.

Hiero's crown, Archimedes added another modern twist to his work: carefully controlled experiment.

Here's how he did it:

Archimedes found that one pound of silver has more volume (in other words, occupies more space) than one pound of gold. Therefore, a certain weight of silver would displace more water than an equal weight of gold. Archimedes obtained a lump of pure gold equal in weight to the crown. He first suspended the solid-gold lump, then the crown, in a brimful tank of water and carefully measured the overflow cause by each. The crown caused more overflow, and, as Vitruvius concludes, "the goldsmith's fraud stood revealed."

Archimedes' Principle, once again, is an idealized mathematical law, and—however dramatic and amusing the bathtub incident—Archimedes developed it from firm mathematical (and experimental) grounds. In his treatise that deals with the subject, *On Floating Bodies,* Archimedes considers the bodies immersed in water as having ideal geometrical volumes and centers of gravity, and the forces at work he sees as acting along geometrically plotted lines. Finally, Archimedes proves the principle as though he were proving a geometrical theorem.

Greek science reached its greatest heights in the work of Archimedes. Some mathematicians believe his mathematical genius has never been equaled, considering the disadvantages under which he worked.

Perhaps even more impressive, Archimedes took the ideal mathematical abstractions of Plato and other Greeks and combined them with the often crude and fumbling physics of Aristotle and Strato. The result, quite literally, was modern physics.

Yet, a disturbing question remains.

Why is it that science waited almost two thousand years to follow where he pointed?

Archimedes Lost . . . and Found Forever

Historians of science regard *On the Method* as one of the greatest "finds" of the twentieth century. Certainly, the circumstances of its discovery would be hard to match in pure drama. And its contents shed light not only on Archimedes and the working of his brilliant mind but on all Greek science.

This tends to overshadow the more recent discovery of another treatise by Archimedes, *The Regular Heptagon,* in 1926. It was found, far less dramatically, in an Arabic manuscript which contained other scientific texts. Though narrower in scope and less revolutionary than *On the Method, The Regular Heptagon* is without question a notable work of Greek geometry.

Here, then, are two important treaties by Archimedes, who, since the Renaissance, has been acclaimed as one of the greatest of all scientists. Both these treatises were lost and unread for hundreds of years and did not become known again until our own century. Furthermore, *The Regular Heptagon* survived only because a studious Arab once translated it from Greek into his native language; and *On the Method* was preserved by a mere fluke. We have it only because a Greek monk deliberately tried to erase it! How could such things happen?

The answer lies in the tides and undercurrents of history.

At the time of his death, Greek science as a whole lagged behind Archimedes. This was natural, because Archimedes had, in a way, been a prophet, and his scientific attitudes could not be assimilated overnight. The Greeks, for example, could not immediately accept his mathematical view of physics. It was too new, and the tradition of Aristotle's and Strato's nonmathematical physics had been too deeply ingrained.

Then, before Greek science could catch up to Archimedes and move as a whole in the direction of modern science, two tremendous forces began working in the Mediterranean. Neither of these forces was conducive to the rise of a modern science based on mathematical and experimental grounds.

One force was the emergence of Christianity. This had a double effect. Christianity mixed a warmer, more spiritual outlook with the abstract, critical thought of the Greeks. More and more, the path of pure reason was looked on as treacherous and ungodly. This attitude may have been good for mankind, but it was not good for Greek science. Also, Christianity drew many fine intellects away from the study of science and into the fight to establish the Church.

The second force was the rise of Rome to a dominant position in the Mediterranean. The Romans were a practical people who placed little value on theoretical science. Instead, they favored applied science and encouraged and rewarded primarily their engineers.

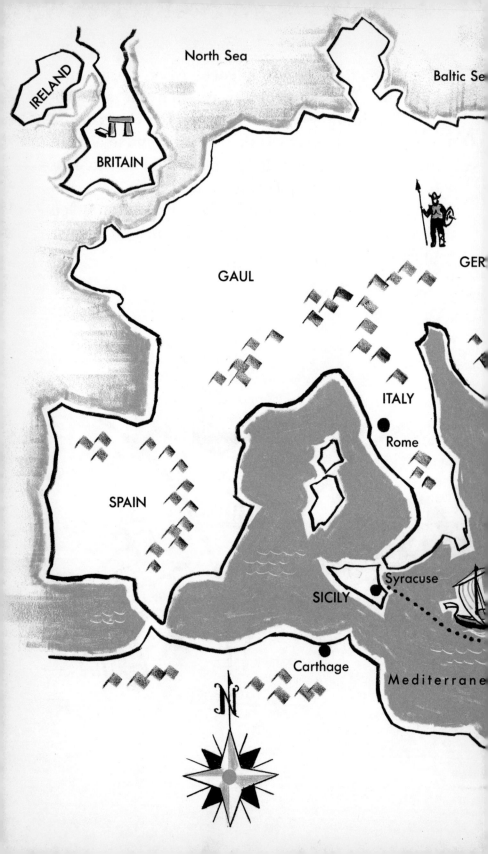

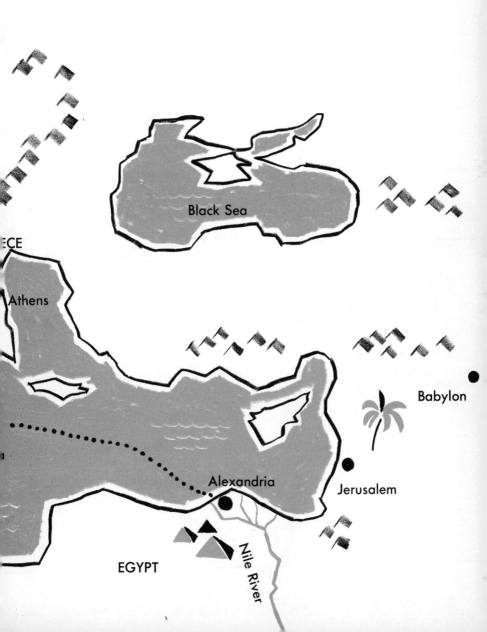

MEDITERRANEAN CIVILIZATION
THIRD CENTURY B.C.

Black Sea

ECE

Athens

Babylon

Alexandria

Jerusalem

EGYPT

Nile River

Undermined on one side by the hostility of the Church, and on the other side by the indifference of the Romans, the golden age of Greek science ended. The works of its great scientists, however, remained.

These ancient works began a long and twisting ascent through the ages. Countless numbers of them would not survive, or would survive only in part.

Ironically, Archimedes' works suffered because of their very modernness. Monks and scribes, naturally, would copy works that they understood and enjoyed. Likewise, scholars would translate or comment upon works that they believed were significant or constructive. Archimedes' work often seemed to have none of these qualities. It seemed too abstract and too "different."

The Greek monk who scratched out *On the Method* had probably found it utterly baffling and almost unintelligible. The description of a church service, he felt, would make far better use of the valuable parchment.

The attitudes of the Romans also worked against Archimedes' treatises. As we know, they had little patience with theoretical science. If they studied pure science at all, they preferred comprehensive, encyclopedia-like collections, such as the writings of Aristotle or Euclid's *Elements*. Self-contained treatises on a single subject, like those of Archimedes, did not appeal to them.

Thus, Archimedes was never a popular author in late ancient times, or in the Middle Ages. His name, it appears, was widely known; but people connected it with a completely distorted image. Archimedes was thought of as a kind of mechanical sorcerer, able to invent incredible things. These beliefs reached a height of absurdity when a mere clockmaker was called "the second Archimedes," and a Swedish inventor "the Swedish Archimedes."

Since few copies of Archimedes' works were made, their chances of survival were proportionately small. There is no telling just how many treatises of Archimedes are lost. Ancient writers mention the names, or subject matter, of several that haven't come down to us.

At least one work on astronomy by Archimedes has been lost, *On Sphere Making.* This apparently describes his highly accurate model of the solar system, his "miniature planetarium." Furthermore, all his work on optics is lost, as is a treatise called *Naming of Numbers.* Also, Archimedes seems to have written a treatise on the compound pulley. If so, it has vanished.

Some of these works—or others that we don't even know about—may eventually reappear. But the chances are small and diminish with every passing year. Ancient manuscripts are vulnerable to any number of fatal accidents: human beings may unwittingly destroy them, or the elements, or simply the decay of time.

It is just possible, say scholars, that lost Archimedean texts may turn up, as *The Regular Heptagon* did, in Arabic translation. The Arabs of the Middle Ages had

Sir Isaac Newton
1642–1727

Galileo
1564–1642

Leonardo Da Vinci
1452–1519

a childlike awe of Greek scientific works and translated hundreds of them, often without any real comprehension of their value. These translations were then lumped together, the good with the bad, in composite manuscripts. One of these may someday be found that contains a lost work of Archimedes. Even this, though, is a dim hope, for time is running out here, too.

Yet, as the great Harvard historian of science George Sarton once said: "The astonishing thing is not that so much Greek science has been lost, but rather that so much has escaped the vicissitudes of time and reached our very hands. . . . It is a 'miracle' that any of Archimedes' works survived at all."

Modern science is deeply thankful for this "miracle."

As the Renaissance began in Europe, ten of Archimedes' treatises were known. By the end of the sixteenth century, all ten had entered print, and thus their preservation was assured for all time.

Ten treatises may sound like a pitifully small collection, and indeed it is, making barely more than three hundred pages of text. But the contents of these ten treatises had a profound influence on the fathers of modern science.

Leonardo da Vinci was one of the first to see the tremendous significance of Archimedes' works and profit from their lessons. Galileo, Newton, and Kepler followed, taking over and extending Archimedes' concepts of mathematical abstraction in physics.

Archimedes' mathematics had a shaping effect on the work of the first great Renaissance mathematician, Descartes; and Archimedes reached far ahead into the nineteenth century, to excite the "boundless admiration" of the brilliant mathematician Karl Gauss.

Perhaps a simple statement of Galileo best expresses the reverent attitude of modern science toward Archimedes. In his book *Dialogue Concerning Two New Sciences,* Galileo at one point is answering an argument against his law for the path of a projectile.

Galileo's law, says a doubter, is an idealized mathematical statement and is therefore not valid. In rebuttal, Galileo begins:

"The authority of Archimedes alone will satisfy everybody . . ."

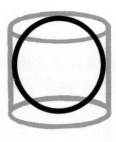

Index